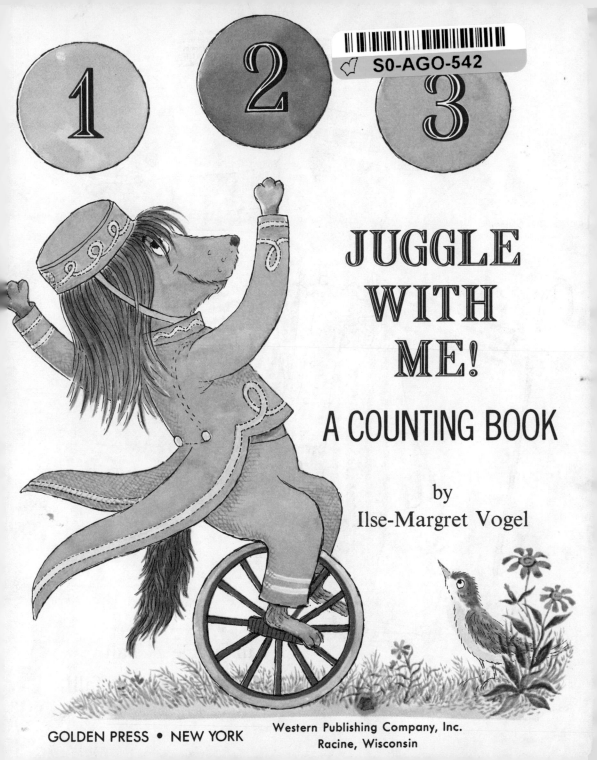

1 2 3

JUGGLE WITH ME!

A COUNTING BOOK

by
Ilse-Margret Vogel

GOLDEN PRESS • NEW YORK

Western Publishing Company, Inc.
Racine, Wisconsin

I can juggle 1 ball
And it does not fall!

Is that all?
Just one ball?

I can do
Much better than you!

Look! I juggle 2

You mean juggling two
Is all you can do?

It's one, two, 3
When I juggle, you see.

One, two, three—
That's nothing for me!

Look, look! I juggle 4

You juggle five
  It's amazing to see
Four fly through the air
  And one bounce on your knee.

I'm in a fix.
I can't juggle 6

You can't juggle six?
That isn't so good.
You should have tried to—
Really, you should.

7 are almost too many for me,
Yet I manage to keep them all going, you see.

He keeps seven going.
 Can you do more?
If you try hard,
 You might beat his score.

I can almost do 8 –
Almost, but not quite.
One ball always falls.
I can't do it right.

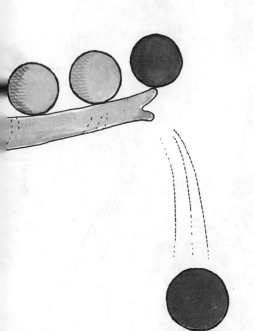

Eight are too many?
I really don't see
How such a thing
Could possibly be.

I'VE GOT NEWS
FOR YOU

I'VE GOT NEWS FOR YOU

FOR YOU

by John Wheeler

E. P. Dutton & Co., Inc.
New York   1961

Library of Congress Catalog Card Number: 61-6015

This book is dedicated lovingly to my late daughter,

ELIZABETH WHEELER ELLISON

CONTENTS

LIST OF ILLUSTRATIONS

(Cartoons)

Sports and characters at the Willard-Moran championship fight, by Clare Briggs, page 18.

Irvin Cobb at the Illustrators' Ball, by Wallace Morgan, page 92.

Brisbane's Park Row Pups, by Tad, page 116.

First *Mutt and Jeff* strip drawn by Bud Fisher in 1907, page 212.

(Photographs, between pages 96 and 97)

Baseball writers covering the New York Giants, 1908.

Richard Harding Davis in the trenches at Salonika.

Mexican troops, including Raul Madero, with Bud Fisher and the author.

General Villa's private railroad car.

Ring Lardner acting as a lion tamer.

President Harding, Grantland Rice, Ring Lardner, and Henry Fletcher before a golf game.

Three lousy golfers: Deac Aylesworth, Roy Howard, and the author.

Captain Eddie Rickenbacker and John Wheeler arriving in Mexico City after first flight of Eastern Air Lines.

Helen Reid, General Leon Johnson, Hugh Baillie, John Wheeler, and Jimmy Doolittle at a state dinner at the Lotus Club, 1954.

John Wheeler.

I. GHOST-WRITING—HOW IT STARTED

WHEN I was an undergraduate at Columbia University, I served as the *New York Herald* correspondent there. One day I decided to investigate a mysterious old guy with a beard whom I noticed hanging around campus and going to classes regularly. He looked to be about 65. I found out his name was Kemp, and I began talking to him one day.

"How come you are still in college?" I asked him.

"Well, you see," he explained, "when my uncle died, he left me a handsome allowance as long as I went to school. If I quit, it was cut off, so I've been here ever since. The only trouble is I am running out of courses to take."

My story got a big play, and the other New York papers tincanned after me. Probably that's why I am in the newspaper business today. When I graduated from Columbia in 1908, I took a job with the *Herald.*

This first newspaper job wasn't too exciting until I got to be a baseball reporter and then became a ghost writer, possibly the first in newspaper history.

I was traveling with the New York Giants in 1911 when I got a wire from my boss, the sports editor, which read about as follows: "Sign up Christy Mathewson to cover the World's Series exclusively. Offer up to $500 but try to get him for less."

This referred to the outstanding pitcher of that day, also known as Matty and Big Six. I looked him up and promptly offered him the $500, telling him it was my limit. He took it since this was a new source of income and ballplayers did not get such big money in those times. I was assigned to confer with Matty after every game and then turn out the expert's masterpieces. The Giants' opponents were the Philadelphia

11

Athletics. A cane-carrying *Herald* staff star named Fitzgerald (not Scott Fitzgerald) was to write the color stuff on the games.

Everything went along well until a gentleman named Frank Baker, who played third base for the Athletics, got hold of one and knocked it over the fence, thus busting up the ball game. A famous left-hander, Rube Marquard, was pitching for the Giants. That night Big Six and I turned out a very informative piece pointing out that the southpaw had served the wrong kind of a ball, and, if he had aimed at Baker's weakness, all would have been jake. As I recall it, Rube should have pitched one on the outside instead of the inside.

This erudite contribution to literature was widely published and stood up very well until the next afternoon when Matty himself, the old master, was in the box. Up came Home-Run Baker with two on. The last seen of the ball was when it disappeared over the center-field bleachers into the street outside. There was considerable razzing from the stands, evidently by some of the fans who had read the article on how to pitch to Baker by Christy Mathewson. We had a tough time working out a story that night, and finally Big Six decided to admit he had thrown a wrong one to Baker, too, and Baker was a great hitter anyway. This was characteristic of Matty's sportsmanship.

In those days, as I recall it, it was the best five out of nine, and about midway of the Series, we got a long rainy spell. I hung around with the ballplayers, and Mathewson and I turned out a dope story every night which made money for my employer, since the *Herald* syndicate was selling the service to other papers at so much a word. The prima donna with the cane came to Philadelphia only in clear weather when there was a game. Much to my surprise, after the Series a notice appeared on the *Herald* bulletin board awarding Fitzgerald a bonus of $25 for his good work in covering the event, while I didn't even get the time of day.

The next winter Christy Mathewson and I wrote a series of weekly articles for the McClure Newspaper Syndicate on "Inside Baseball." This sold very well. Subsequently, the collection was published in book form by Putnam. The title was *Pitching in a Pinch*. Matty and I each had a half interest. It kept on selling even after he died, and I then turned my share of the royalties over to Mrs. Mathewson. It was a damn good book.

When it was published I was still working on the *New York Herald* as a baseball writer, and there was a nice old fellow named James Ford who did the book reviews. I watched closely to see if *Pitching in a Pinch* was mentioned, but no soap. One day I met Mr. Ford in the hall and stopped him. I am not sure he even knew I worked on the paper, because he operated from a kind of ivory tower out front.

"Have you read the Christy Mathewson book *Pitching in a Pinch?*" I asked him.

He seemed slightly puzzled.

"No, I haven't," he answered.

"I thought maybe you would like to review it," I suggested.

"Have you read it?" he came back. "Could you review it for me?"

Had I read it? I could practically recite it and so could my whole family. I let myself go, and I very much doubt whether any book ever got a more favorable review.

In 1913, after the *Herald* turned down my request for a raise, I left and started an organization modestly called the Wheeler Syndicate. I hired Matty and a lot of other ballplayers for winter articles and covering important games. I was the most active spook practicing. Besides the book for Christy Mathewson, I wrote a later one for Ty Cobb entitled

Busting 'Em. In one World Series I was turning out expert copy for about eight stars.

The idea spread, and the old *Tribune* signed up Wild Bill Donovan, the American League pitching star, to expert for it. Bill MacBeth was his ghost.

Bill didn't believe in handicapping himself by getting the ideas of his star, so he wrote a story for publication on the opening day predicting the Boston Braves would beat the Athletics in four straight. Philadelphia was a heavy favorite, for it had a team made up of great players with big reputations who were supposed to scare their opponents as soon as they walked on the field. Donovan, being an American Leaguer, was searching for MacBeth with murder on his mind. He insisted MacBeth's prediction was ridiculous and made him look bad.

Boston won the first game, and Donovan began to cool off a little. After the Braves came through in the second, Donovan stuck his chest out and praised himself as a prophet. When they won four straight, he claimed MacBeth had had nothing to do with the prediction—that it was all his.

Eddie Collins, who was playing second base for the Athletics, and I went to college together, and I made him an offer before the Series, but he got a better one and took it, which was all right with me and part of the racket. We did sign up Johnny Evers, the fiery little second sacker for the Braves.

"Is Collins writing for you?" he asked me.

"No," I replied, "he got a better proposition than we made him."

After the Series, Evers was telling me how they rode the Athletics.

"We had that Collins so up in the air he couldn't spit and hit the ground," boasted Evers. He meant when a fellow gets nervous, his mouth dries up.

"What did you ride him about?" I asked him.

"We kept yelling, 'So you would throw down an old pal for fifty bucks, you cheapskate.' "

"Who was the pal?" I asked innocently.

"Why you were," explained Johnny with a laugh.

One of my saddest experiences was with Big Jess Willard, the prizefighter. We had signed him before his bout in Toledo with Jack Dempsey for the heavyweight championship, and I was to be the boy behind the typewriter as usual. We knocked out some good preliminary stories together which didn't give the challenger a chance—Dempsey was too small and all that. Willard foolishly let Jack Kearns talk him into bandaging their hands outside the ring. The Champion was trying to save money and doing his own managing.

The night before the battle Willard visited Tex Rickard, the promoter, to talk about his future plans. According to reliable reports, during the discussion he consumed a bottle of gin. Even an old-timer like Tex was surprised.

"Ain't that pretty strong medicine you're training on?" he asked.

"Don't worry," replied Big Jess, "I'll only be in there for exercise tomorrow. Jack's too little to hurt me."

The day was scorching hot—July 4, 1919. I was to meet Willard right after the fight in his dressing room to get his ideas. The first round was a bloody one. Dempsey, in perfect condition, laid his opponent's face open with nearly every blow he hit him. He cut him to ribbons. This led to the false report he had something besides fists inside his gloves, like Plaster of Paris or tire tape. Jess looked as if he had passed through a meat grinder.

There was also a rumor Dempsey and his manager, Jack Kearns, had bet $10,000 against $100,000 the battle would not last more than one round. It was close. With Willard on the deck, the referee counted him out, and the challenger rushed from the ring to his dressing room, thinking he had won. The timekeeper in the excitement had either forgotten to pull the string or Ollie Pecord, the referee, had not heard the bell. If Willard had had a smart man in his corner who could have claimed the decision on the grounds Dempsey had departed from the premises, it might have been different. The fight finally ended as the bell rang for the fourth round with our man a battered hulk and bleeding from practically every pore. His seconds threw in the towel.

After taking one or two looks at him, I realized he wouldn't have any ideas for a week or ten days, unless it would be to cut out some paper dolls. I didn't even go to his dressing room, but wrote the best story I could on my own. There wasn't much to say except about the devastating power of Jack Dempsey's punches. At the end I had Willard express the hope he would live.

Another worn-out fighter, Battling Nelson, had been assigned by the *Chicago Daily News* to cover the championship fight. By this time the poor fellow was punch drunk.

For some reason, Nelson set up housekeeping in a tent out by the arena where the contest was to take place, although this location was miles from the scene of the preliminary activities. Maybe he thought the promoters might try to hold the contest secretly some night, and he would be on hand. Even though it was during Prohibition, some of the other boys used to celebrate pretty good with the help of Jack Kearns, Dempsey's manager. Along about 2 o'clock in the morning somebody would suggest—usually Tad, the cartoonist—that they go out and visit Nelson. This consisted of approaching his tent stealthily and pulling out the pegs which naturally made it collapse. The culprits would escape before he could untangle himself.

The old battler, being a cleanly fellow, used to walk down to near-by Lake Erie armed with a towel and a cake of soap and take his morning bath. The weather the day of the fight was frightfully hot. The concessionaire had moved several barrels of lemonade out near the arena the night before, anticipating a rushing business. Nelson arose as usual the morning of the battle and headed for the lake.

However, on the way, he saw a hogshead filled with what he thought was nice clean water, so being in a hurry and having a busy day ahead, he hopped into it, soaped himself off, and finished his bath. He told several friends of his good fortune, and the word spread through the crowd that Battling Nelson had doused himself in the lemonade. Of course, there was no way of telling which barrel had entertained him. The result was nearly everyone steered clear of the drink, and the concessionaire was practically ruined.

Ring Lardner got a release from his *Chicago Tribune* contract in time to cover the Dempsey-Willard brawl for us. Also out in Toledo was Ring Lardner's shadow and a faint carbon copy of his literary output, a fellow named H. C. Witwer. Tad got to addressing Ring as "Witwer" and vice versa. Witwer is dead now and so is Lardner, but it is my bet if they arrived at the same destination, he is still following Ring around and eavesdropping.

Irvin Cobb, the humorist, was discussing Witwer's talents with Charles Hanson Towne, then the editor of *McClure's Magazine* which was publishing some of the author's stories.

"Don't you think Witwer is a good writer?" asked Towne.

"I am not sure about him being a good writer," replied Cobb, "but I do know he is a damned close reader."

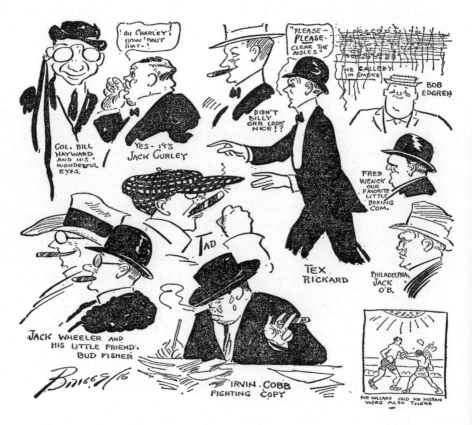

Cartoon by Clare Briggs showing some of the sports and characters attending the fight for the world championship between Jess Willard and Frank Moran. (Clare Briggs)